This book is dedicated to
Dilgo Khyentse Rinpoche
- past, present and future -
May I always be near you.

Also to Dorkya Tulku and Tashi Chime
for their stoicism in enduring so many
boring English classes...

# NOW I KNOW...

That it's better to face my monsters.

by Sally Devorsine

First printing 2011. ISBN: 978-0-9740268-2-4

THE DALAI LAMA

## ENDORSEMENT

Geshe Langri Thangpa (1054—1123 CE) was a Buddhist master famous in Tibet for his 'Eight Verses of Mind Training'. He originally wrote them down for his own personal use, but they have later become an invaluable guide for many other practitioners down the centuries. The proof of their worth is that these practical instructions on how to make oneself and others happy in everyday situations are just as relevant today, for both adults and children, as they were nearly 1,000 years ago. This I can say from my own experience, for I myself was introduced to them when I was a young boy and I have recited them every day since then. When I meet with difficult circumstances, I reflect on their meaning and I find it helpful.

Sally Devorsine teaches English in Bhutan to the young reincarnation of a lama who was one of my own esteemed teachers, Dilgo Khyentse Rinpoche. She was inspired by the verses of Langri Thangpa to create these colourful storybooks, initially to entertain her young student. Later, she realised that they might provide a way to introduce some of the longstanding values that we Tibetans hold dear to children elsewhere in the world today.

If we are to ensure a peaceful future for our world, I believe that it is important that we foster positive values like compassion, kindness and love in our children's minds from an early age. Certainly books like these can help us do that. Each of these stories shows the young reader a different way to secure happiness, whether it is by recognising anger when it arises, being aware of how our every action has an effect on others, or looking beyond our first impressions of people we meet.

I congratulate Sally Devorsine on her efforts and hope that these charming books have the edifying result she intended. I am sure they will delight readers young and old.

March 25, 2011

So, I really thought long and hard about it,
and then I tried to explain how it felt.

I I want to be a good boy,
I I want to be calm and quiet,
I I want to listen carefully...
I hate causing such a riot!

So, I felt a bit embarassed, but...

I tried... and I tried... and I tried... and I tried...

This time,
before he even appeared,
I welcomed him.

"Hello!"

And, when he
did show his face,
he was sitting
on a flower,
breathing
calmly.

I realized then, that if I welcomed him the moment he arrived,
I would be in control! I would be able to tame him!
He wouldn't be able to sneak up behind me anymore!

So, I'm happy to say I didn't see him much after that...

And I didn't miss him much at all.

# A little bit extra at the end...

1. Look at the front cover of the book. Why is Timmo bowing to the monster? Who do you think has the most power in this picture, Timmo or his monster?

2. Do you think it is better to push our monsters away, or meet them face to face? Why?

3. Have you ever lost control? What happened?

4. Have you ever seen someone else who has lost control?
   How did they look?
   Try to draw your own "out of control" monster.
   Is it big or small? Mischievous or frightening? Human or animal (or alien!)? What colour is it?

5. Why did Timmo expect his teacher to be angry with him when he told her about the monster?

6. How did Timmo's teacher welcome the monster? Why do you think she did that?

7. Why do you think the monster began to come less and less after he was welcomed by Timmo, Ms. Wisely and the rest of the class?

8. Are Timmo and his monster two different people, or one and the same?

In all activities, may I examine my mind,
And as soon as conflicting emotions arise
Endangering myself and others,
May I firmly face and avert them.

Langri Thangpa (1054–1123)

This book is one of a series of eight books
from the "Now I Know..." series.

Each book is based upon one of the eight verses of mind training
written by the 11th century Tibetan Buddhist master, Langri Thangpa.

Each verse, written in the back of the book, offers a different method
for finding happiness, both for ourselves and for others too.

Now I Know...That I wouldn't be who I think I am, without other people.

Now I Know...That I'm not, actually, Mr. Wonderful.

Now I Know..That it's better to face my monsters.

Now I Know...That we all have a jewel inside us somewhere.

Now I Know...That I just have to look for the root and yank it out.

Now I Know...That silly hopes and fears will just make wrinkles on my face.

Now I Know...That it's better to keep quiet about the good things I do (and shout about the bad)

Now I know...That I just have to keep my eye on the ball.